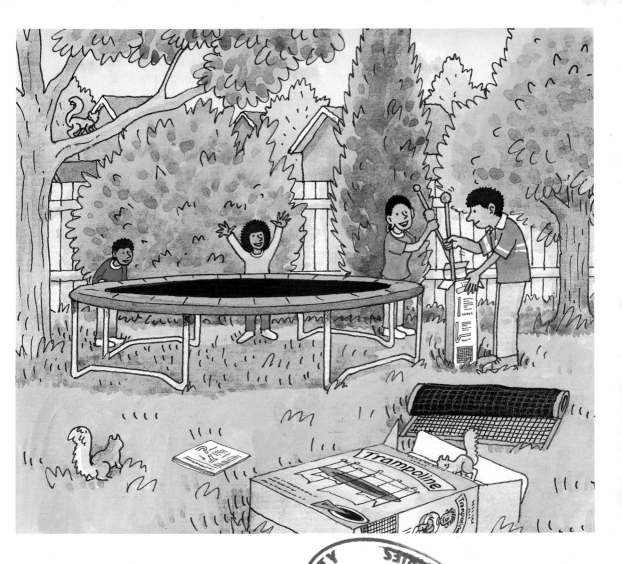

Wilma and Wilf had a trampoline.

D0522719

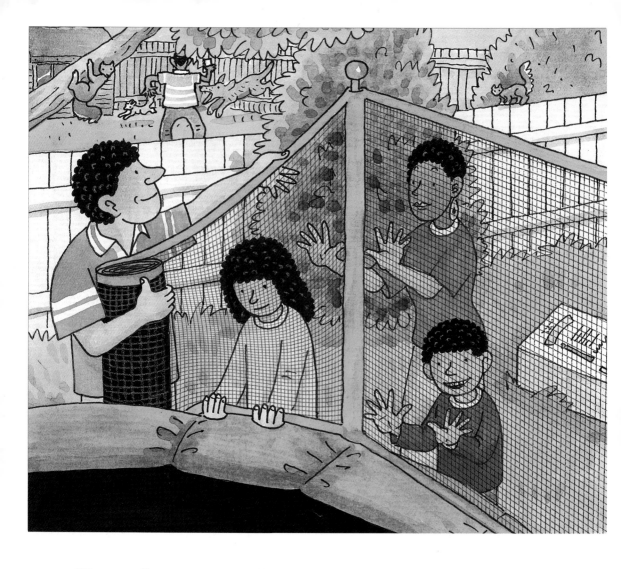

Dad put the net up.

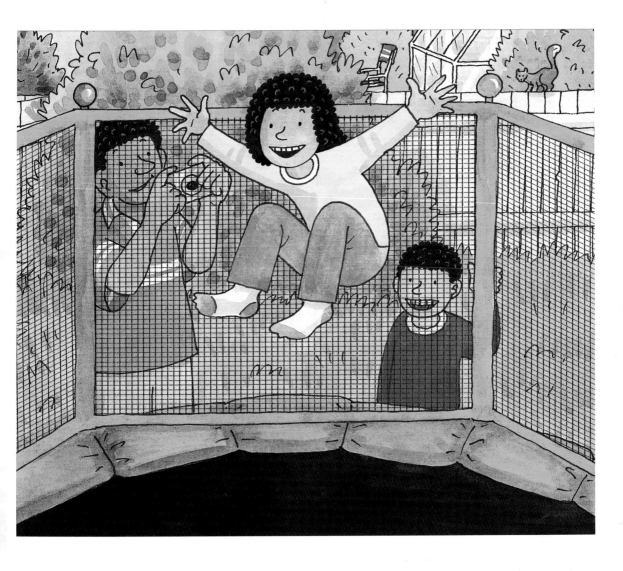

Wilma got on. She went up
and down.

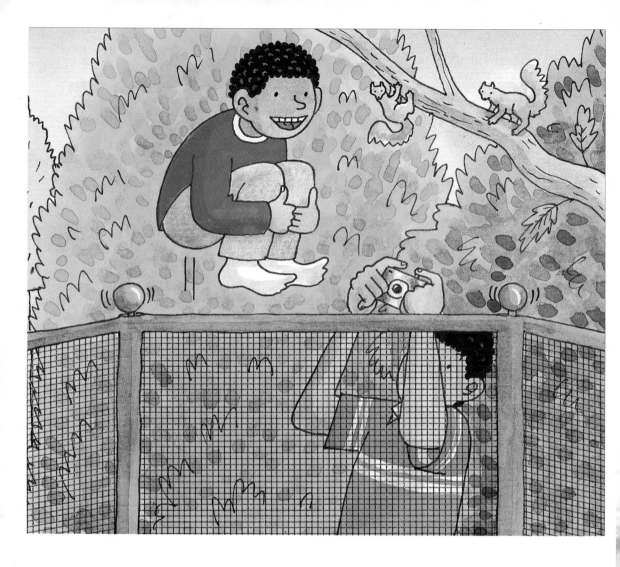

Wilf got on. Up and down he went.

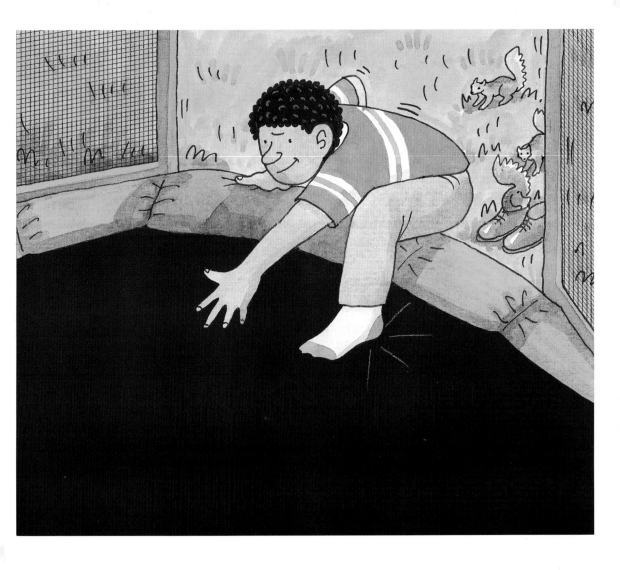

Dad got on the trampoline.

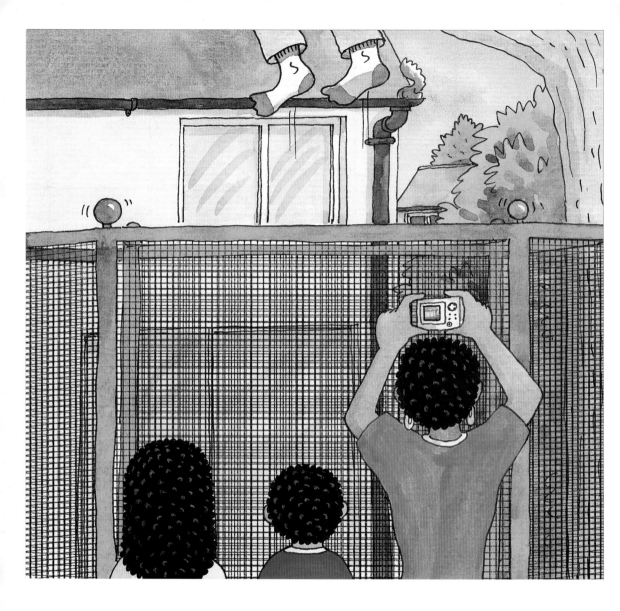

Up he went . . .

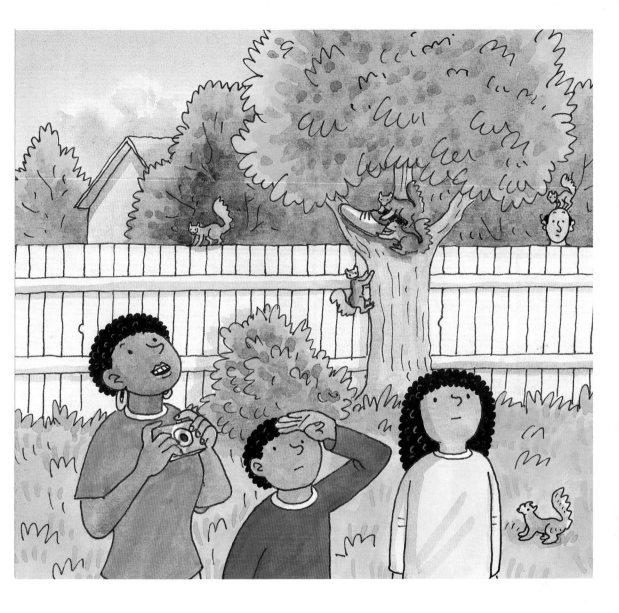

. . . but not down.

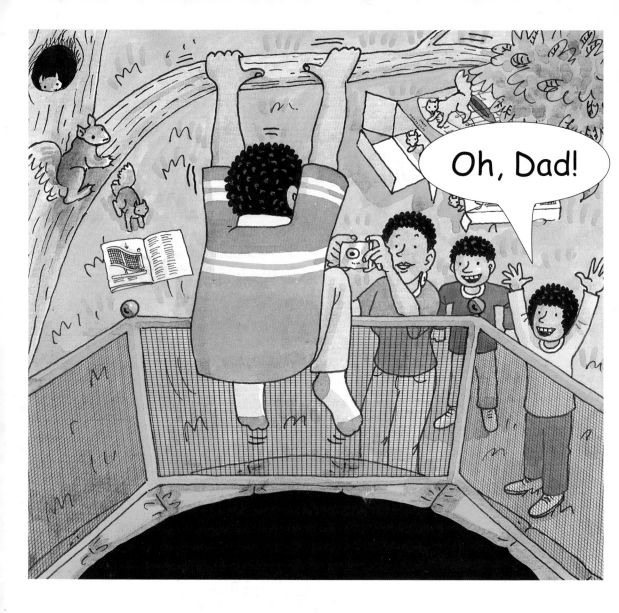